or Tails?

Bill Holt
Illustrated by Giovannina Colalillo

Contents

1 A Big Problem 2

2 A Great Idea 6

3 The Experiment 11

4 Maybe Dad Can Help 14

5 Did We Really Win? 18

6 Will We Win Again? 22

7 An Amazing Play 26

8 A Surprise on the Sidelines 30

Rigby®

A Big Problem

At dinner Suwon sadly played with the pieces of cabbage and radish in her *kimchi* instead of eating them, which was not like Suwon at all. She loved *kimchi* and was usually very cheerful, especially on days when her soccer team—the Tigers—played a game. Nothing made her happier than racing around the grassy field with her friends, trying to score goals.

But tonight Suwon was miserable. The Tigers had lost their game, and Suwon was sure that it was her fault. It had been up to Suwon to win the coin toss this afternoon in order to choose which net their team would defend first.

Everyone in Suwon's soccer league was convinced that the team that defended the lucky net at the beginning of a game—and shot into it at the end—would win the game. At last week's game, the first of the season, Suwon had won the coin toss and claimed the lucky net for her team. After that game, her teammates had decided that Suwon would always call the coin toss. But today she had lost the coin toss, and the Tigers had lost the game.

"Is something wrong, Suwon?" Mom asked, worried. Suwon shook her head, wishing she *could* explain her problem to Mom, but she didn't think Mom would understand.

When Mom was growing up in South Korea, her older brother (Suwon's Uncle Yee-Tai) had shown her how to play soccer. He was such a great player that now he played in a major soccer league in Korea.

Uncle Yee-Tai had taught Mom many amazing soccer tricks, and she'd been the star player of her neighborhood soccer team back in South Korea. When Suwon's family moved to the United States, one of the first things Mom did was to find a new soccer team to join. Then Mom became the star of *that* team, the Rockets.

Neither Uncle Yee-Tai nor Mom needed a lucky net to play well. Suwon believed that her team couldn't possibly win *without* the lucky net . . . but she could *never* admit that to Mom!

A Great Idea

For the next few days, Suwon had trouble eating, sleeping, and even paying attention at school because she was so busy thinking about how she could be sure to win the coin toss. On Wednesday night, Mom had to remind Suwon three times that there was a letter from Uncle Yee-Tai waiting on the hall table for her. Finally Suwon opened it.

Yee-Tai Kwan
146-1 Joongang-Dong
Kwachun City, Kyoungki-do
South Korea 427-760

Suwon Jin
8365 Tree Rd.
Dallas, TX 75206
USA

Dear Suwon,

I am coming from South Korea to the United States for a visit next month, and I can't wait to watch you play soccer! Your mom told me that you won your first game, and she is very proud of you. I hope she is teaching you all of the tricks that I showed her many years ago.

Love,
Uncle Yee-Tai

Suwon sadly placed the letter down on the table. Normally this would have been great news for Suwon— but not now!

Suwon just *had* to find a way for her team to defend the lucky net first when Uncle Yee-Tai came to visit, and then the Tigers would definitely win! She needed to be certain that she would always win the coin toss.

Suwon took a quarter out of her pocket and stared at it thoughtfully. How could she determine whether the coin would be more likely to land on heads or tails at the next game? Suwon tossed the quarter in the air, and suddenly she had a great idea.

The Experiment

On the morning of the Tigers' next game, Suwon asked her friend Belinda to come over to help her with an unusual project. Belinda hurried right over. However, once she found out what the project was, she wanted to leave.

"Anything is better than flipping a coin over and over," Belinda said.

"Please, Belinda, you've got to help me," Suwon begged. "If I win the coin toss at the next game, then I can pick the lucky net for my team."

Belinda knew how important the soccer team was to Suwon, so she sighed and sat back down. Suwon flipped the quarter ten times, and Belinda tallied the results on a chart. There were seven marks under *Heads* and three marks under *Tails*. When Suwon saw the results, she was certain that she should call heads at the next game.

At the game, Suwon calmly walked across the field to the referee, convinced that she would win.

"Heads!" she shouted when the coin flipped up into the air, and she closed her eyes tightly, waiting for the referee to announce the result.

"Tails!" the referee called, and the other team chose to defend the lucky net first as Suwon sadly walked away.

Suwon could not stop thinking about how she had lost the coin toss and let down her teammates. While she was wondering what could have gone wrong with her experiment, the ball slid right past her feet. To make matters worse, she accidentally kicked the ball out of bounds. As she thought to herself, "This must all be because I lost the coin toss," the ball whirled by her legs so fast that she tripped and fell flat on her face. By the time she climbed to her feet the game had ended, and the other team had won.

Maybe Dad Can Help

On the way home, Mom again asked Suwon if something was troubling her. Embarrassed by how terribly she had played, Suwon just looked down and tried to wipe the smears of grass and dirt off the front of her shirt, mumbling, "I'm fine, but I've got to play better next week."

Mom was still worried, but she couldn't get Suwon to tell her what was wrong. She guessed that Suwon was upset that the Tigers had lost. Mom decided to ask Dad to talk to Suwon, hoping Suwon would tell *him* about her problem.

After dinner Dad found Suwon sitting in the family room, staring at a quarter. "Suwon," Dad said gently, "you didn't seem to be having much fun during your soccer game today. Is everything OK?"

Suwon didn't want to tell anyone about her problem—even Dad—but she knew that she needed help. Maybe she could get Dad's advice without telling him her *whole* problem. "I *wasn't* having fun today, Dad. I was thinking about an experiment I did. The results it predicted turned out to be wrong, so now I'm trying to figure out how to make them right."

Dad replied, "Sometimes it takes *many* experiments to get good results. I think you'd better try your experiment again. I'm sure you'll get better results if you give yourself many more chances."

Suwon immediately knew what she needed to do. On the next game day, she would invite Belinda over and perform the experiment again . . . but with more tosses this time.

Did We Really Win?

"You want to count a hundred tosses?" Belinda asked, her eyes widening in shock. "But I have to be home in an hour for my violin lesson!"

Suwon told Belinda that it wouldn't take that long and begged her to help. Groaning, Belinda gave in. When they were finished, Belinda even made a bar graph of the results: 49 heads and 51 tails.

Suwon loudly called "Tails!" during the coin toss at the game, positive that she would win. However, this time the quarter landed on heads! Once again the Tigers had lost the lucky net. Suwon was sad at first, but then she thought, "Maybe Belinda and I just need to do *more* experiments to get even *better* results."

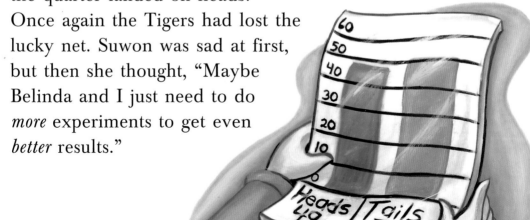

There was nothing Suwon could do about that for now, so she decided to focus on the game. The Tigers were playing well, and everyone seemed to be having fun. Suwon skillfully moved about the field, dribbling and passing to her teammates.

At halftime the teams switched nets, but Suwon was
enjoying the game so much that she had forgotten all
about the coin toss and the lucky net. The game was tied,
and then Esteban stole the ball from the other team,
sending it flying into the net in the final seconds of the
game, and the Tigers won!

"That's odd. We won even without the lucky net,"
Suwon thought suddenly.

Will We Win Again?

On the morning of the next game, Belinda laughed in disbelief when she heard that Suwon wanted to count a *thousand* coin tosses. Suwon pleaded for Belinda to stay, reminding her that Uncle Yee-Tai was coming all the way from South Korea to visit next Saturday. This was Suwon's last chance to test whether she'd be able to predict correctly whether to call heads or tails at the coin toss.

Belinda sighed and agreed to help one last time. Suwon flipped the coin over and over until her thumb was sore and her eyes grew tired from looking at its shiny sides. Finally she finished a thousand tosses, but when she saw Belinda's results, she was astonished. "500 heads and 500 tails? That doesn't tell me anything!"

"Maybe it *does* tell you something," Belinda said thoughtfully. "Maybe it doesn't matter how many times you toss a coin. You'll still never know what the next toss will be. It could be heads *or* tails!"

Just then Dad knocked at Suwon's bedroom door to tell her it was time to start getting ready for her game. Dragging him inside, Suwon showed him the chart and asked if Belinda was right. Was it true that no matter how many times you toss a coin, you can never know what the next toss will be? Dad explained that Belinda was correct, and then asked Suwon why it mattered. He listened quietly while Suwon explained her whole problem. Suwon concluded, "And now I have no way to be sure that my team will win next week when Uncle Yee-Tai visits!"

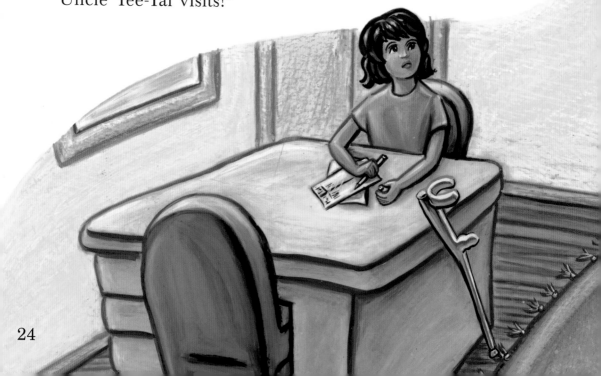

"Suwon, Uncle Yee-Tai doesn't care if the Tigers win or lose. He just wants to see you play," Dad smiled. "Now why don't you stop worrying about lucky nets and start having fun again?"

An Amazing Play

With Dad's words still on her mind, Suwon stepped onto the soccer field that afternoon and felt a warm breeze blow over her face. She could smell the fresh scent of the newly-cut green grass beneath her soccer shoes and hear the roar of the fans stomping on the benches, clapping their hands, and shouting "Go Tigers!" Maybe Dad was right: it didn't matter whether the Tigers won or lost, as long as she had fun playing.

She let the other team, the Ravens, call the coin toss, and once again the Tigers were playing without the lucky net. But this time Suwon didn't let it bother her, and she focused her attention on having fun and playing as well as she could.

The Ravens were a good team, and at halftime the Tigers were losing by two points. While this was the hardest game the Tigers had played so far, it was also the most fun. All of Suwon's teammates were playing well, and they were working together.

Right before the end of the game, Suwon started dribbling the ball swiftly toward the Ravens' net. The goalie thought Suwon was going to try to score and quickly prepared to block her. But at the last moment, Suwon suddenly passed the ball to Esteban, who kicked it right between the goalie's legs and into the net. The play happened so fast that the Ravens' goalie didn't even know what had happened. A second later, the referee's whistle blew, and the game was over.

The Tigers' fans jumped out of their seats and cheered loudly. They had still lost the game, but their final play was amazing! Running toward her parents in excitement, Suwon suddenly stopped in shock. Uncle Yee-Tai was standing next to Mom and Dad!

A Surprise on the Sidelines

"Uncle Yee-Tai, what are you doing here?" Suwon gasped in surprise.

Grinning, Uncle Yee-Tai explained that he'd started his vacation a week earlier than he had planned. "I came straight from the airport to the soccer field to see my favorite niece play!"

Suwon sighed sadly and said, "I wish you'd seen a better game."

Uncle Yee-Tai just smiled and asked, "Suwon, why do you think this was a bad game? You and your friend worked very well together to score that last goal, didn't you?"

Suwon admitted that they had, but then pointed out that they had lost the game anyway. Uncle Yee-Tai laughed and assured her that even *his* team didn't win every game.

"And mine doesn't win all the time either," said Mom, adding that it didn't matter to her whether the Tigers won or lost. Either way she was proud of the way Suwon played.

Suwon confessed that she'd been afraid that Mom and Uncle Yee-Tai would be disappointed in her if her team lost. Mom smiled and said, "Suwon, you could never disappoint me!"

Relieved, Suwon cheerfully followed her family to the car. She knew that she would never worry about lucky nets or winning again. However, it couldn't hurt to have Uncle Yee-Tai teach her some tricks before next week's game!